ILLUSTRATED
SPEECH ANATOMY

By **WILLIAM M. SHEARER, Ph.D.**

Professor of Speech
Northern Illinois University
DeKalb, Illinois

Second Edition

ILLUSTRATED SPEECH ANATOMY

CHARLES C THOMAS · PUBLISHER

Springfield · Illinois · U.S.A.

611.2
S 539

Published and Distributed Throughout the World by
CHARLES C THOMAS • PUBLISHER
BANNERSTONE HOUSE
301-327 East Lawrence Avenue, Springfield, Illinois, U.S.A.
NATCHEZ PLANTATION HOUSE
735 North Atlantic Boulevard, Fort Lauderdale, Florida, U.S.A.

First Edition, 1963
Second Edition, 1968

With THOMAS BOOKS *careful attention is given to all details of
manufacturing and design. It is the Publisher's desire to present books
that are satisfactory as to their physical qualities and artistic possibilities
and appropriate for their particular use.* THOMAS BOOKS *will be true
to those laws of quality that assure a good name and good will.*

Printed in the United States of America
RV-1

PREFACE

Teachers and students in the field of speech have long felt the need for a simple, well illustrated, anatomy text which deals exclusively with the structures involved in respiration, phonation, articulation, and resonance.

It is the purpose of this book to meet such a need in the form of an inexpensive volume containing large, uncluttered illustrations with a minimum of discussion. The bones and muscles are presented in a clear and systematic manner so as to allow for maximum accessibility in study and reference.

Some of the more detailed parts of the total speech structure have purposely been omitted for the sake of clarity. However, instructors who wish to pursue certain anatomical structures in greater detail will find that the present illustrations provide a relatively unobstructed framework for drawing in further additions.

Comments following the illustrations are intended to provide basic information relating to the total speech process, as well as to bring out additional highlights of particular interest.

Throughout the entire text an effort has been made to present anatomy in a visual and graphic framework, and to link the individual structures into a functioning speech system. The exercises will be particularly helpful in this respect. Such an approach is intended to counteract the tendency to deal with anatomy in terms of word lists and rote memory.

Muscle groups are categorized according to speech function and a sub-index is provided in each section for convenient references. The sub-indexes also include the muscle attachments, with the origins being listed first in order, and the insertions following.

In the development of the text, a preliminary edition consisting of fifty-two pages was printed and used as a teaching aid. (The author is grateful to Mr. James Larson of the Duplicating Department, Northern Illinois University, for his helpful consultation and effort in the original offset printing.) During the trial period of the text discrepancies and inaccuracies were corrected and considerably more material was added. In instances where the information might still be considered controversial or experimental an effort was made to present only the simplest and most direct descriptions. The author wishes to thank the following professors and their students for their participation and criticism of the original text: Mr. James

Curtiss, Northern Illinois University; Dr. Bernard Jackson, Eastern Carolina College; and Miss Joan Sayre, Miami University of Ohio.

In addition, the author wishes to thank Dr. Mildred Berry of Rockford College, Rockford, Illinois; Mr. R. Scott Johnson of Marshall University, Huntington, West Virginia; Dr. Ralph Lahaie of Madison College, Harrisonburg, Virginia; Dr. John O'Neil of University of Illinois, and Mr. Stanley Weisberger of New York State University, College of Education, Oneonta, New York, for their helpful comments and encouragement.

Finally, the author wishes to mention his appreciation and thanks to Mr. Gene Norris, Northern Illinois University, for his reading of the completed manuscript.

W. M. S.

ADDENDUM TO PREFACE
(Second Edition)

The Second Edition represents a complete revision of the written text on Phonation and the addition of an entirely new section on the Anatomy of the Ear. The chapter on Phonation has been rewritten to provide a considerably more accurate and detailed description of the varying influence of the vocal cords on the pitch and quality of speech. The section on the Anatomy of the Ear has been added in order to meet the needs of a course in anatomy which covers both speech and hearing. It intends to probe a bit deeper into the topic of functional auditory anatomy than that usually found in beginning audiology texts, but strives to preserve the same simplicity in descriptive style which characterized the first edition.

W.M.S.

CONTENTS

ILLUSTRATED
SPEECH ANATOMY

1

RESPIRATION

BREATHING

Although breathing is a natural and usually quite automatic process, its nature needs to be thoroughly understood by those who are concerned with speech. Voice coaches who tell us that we should speak or sing from the stomach are not anatomically correct, but are nevertheless very helpful in producing better breathing habits. It is the muscles of the abdomen rather than the shoulders which are mainly responsible for the smooth flow of air from the lungs. It is true that raising the *rib cage* will also increase the capacity of the lungs, but the major share of this work is accomplished easier and more smoothly by the *diaphragm* and muscles of the abdomen.

In most effective breathing the shoulders should be straight but not pushed forcibly back. The stomach should push out slightly on inhale and pull in on exhale. Elevation of the *ribs* also helps increase the capacity of the lungs, but excessive raising of the shoulders tends to introduce jerkiness in the speech flow. This is called *clavicular breathing* and is sometimes associated with anxiety.

Individuals having neuromuscular disorders, such as cerebral palsy sometimes employ a pattern of *oppositional breathing,*[1] which means that the ribs raise to the inhale position at the same time that the stomach pulls in to exhale. The result is extremely shallow breathing together with a very inefficient expenditure of energy.

Breathing exercises, as part of a remedial or public speaking program, are no longer as popular as they were in the earlier days of the elocution teacher. However, they may still be used to great advantage in dealing with cerebral palsy[2] or in increasing vocal intensity.[3]

---

[1] C. Van Riper: *Speech Correction,* Third Edition. New York, Prentice-Hall, Inc., 1954.
[2] H. Westlake and D. Rutherford: *Speech Therapy for the Cerebral Palsied.* Chicago, National Society for Crippled Children and Adults, Inc., 1960.
[3] C. Van Riper and J. Irwin: *Voice and Articulation.* Englewood Cliffs, Prentice-Hall, Inc., 1958.

ACTION OF THE DIAPHRAGM IN RESPIRATION

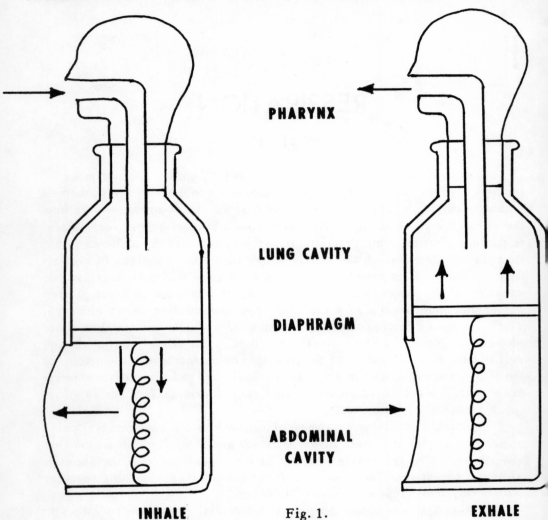

PHARYNX

LUNG CAVITY

DIAPHRAGM

ABDOMINAL
CAVITY

INHALE   Fig. 1.   EXHALE

When we *inhale* the diaphragm pulls down against the stomach, pushing it forward against the abdominal muscles, and making more space for the lungs. This increased space is immediately filled by air forced in under pressure of the atmosphere. In proper deep inhaling the stomach should be slightly protruded.

When we *exhale* the abdominal muscles pull in against the stomach. The stomach, in turn, is forced upward against the diaphragm as it relaxes. This decreases the size of the lung cavity, forcing the air out. Strictly speaking, we do not use our diaphragm during actual phonation, since speech normally occurs during exhalation, when the diaphragm is relaxing.

ACTION OF THE RIBS IN RESPIRATION

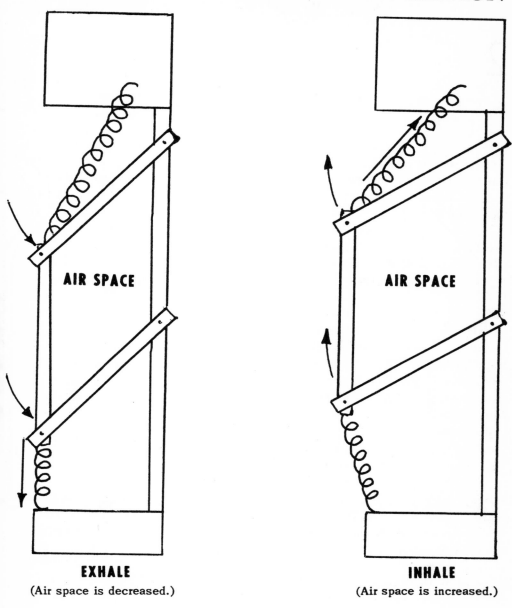

EXHALE
(Air space is decreased.)

INHALE
(Air space is increased.)

Fig. 2. When we inhale, the ribs are raised upward and foreward in order to enlarge the air space inside the rib cage. When we exhale the ribs are pulled downward and inward. Forced exhalation employs the powerful muscles of the stomach. Relaxation and the pull of gravity, however, are sufficient to lower the ribs for normal light breathing.

2

THE SKELETON

In order to understand the purpose of specific muscles, a basic concept of the skeletal structure and action must first be obtained. Since the names of most muscles denote their position and function with respect to the bones of the skeleton, the muscles can be understood only when their attachments are visualized.

For those in the speech field one of the primary interests in the skeleton concerns the rib cage. Basically, all muscles which raise the ribs are muscles of inhalation. Those which pull the ribs down are muscles of exhalation. In normal quiet breathing the pull of gravity is usually sufficient to lower the rib cage, and the muscles of exhalation are then used only slightly. Greater use of the exhalation muscles is employed in forced exhalation following exercise, or when a stronger air stream is required in order to obtain louder speech. It is interesting to note that the *ilium* or pelvic bone, in combination with the *ribs* and *lumbar vertebrae,* tends to enclose the abdominal cavity at the back and sides, leaving the large frontal area of abdominal muscles without skeletal re-enforcement. The front abdominal wall is therefore allowed maximum flexibility in inhalation and exhalation. This same flexibility, however, may allow the stomach to protrude permanently as the muscles become stretched through increased body weight and lack of exercise.

The *spinal column* is relatively rigid except for the *cervical* and *lumbar vertebrae.* Any bending of the body takes place almost entirely within the five large lumbar vertebrae, and many muscles employed in speech as well as for the support of the body are concentrated in this critical area. Poor posture and improper lifting may easily result in aching and fatigue in this large concentration of back muscles. Most of the speech muscles in the lumbar area are employed in exhalation.

The *hyoid bone* is the only bone in the body which does not attach directly to the rest of the skeleton. It is supported by the *greater cornu* of the *thyroid cartilage,* and provides a base for the tongue and many of the muscles of articulation. This horseshoe-shaped bone may be found by rubbing the fingertips directly above the sides of the *larynx.*

BONES OF THE SKELETON

BONE	Muscle attachments (related to speech)	PAGE
Alveolus		11
Atlas	*levator scapulae*	10
Axis	*levator scapulae, medial scalene*	10
Cervicle vertebrae	*scalene (2nd through 7th), levator scapulae (1st through 4th)*	10
Clavicle	*pectoralis major, sterno cleido mastoideus*	9
Coccyx		9,10
Floating ribs		9
Frontal Bone		9,11,12
Humerus	*latissimus dorsi, pectoralis major*	10
Hyoid	*geniohyoid, hyoglossus, mylohyoid, omohyoid, sternohyoid, stylohyoid*	9
Illium (pelvic bone)	*external oblique, internal oblique, latissimus dorsi, quadratus lumborum, transverse abdominis*	9,10
Lumbar vertebrae	*latissimus dorsi, quadratus lumborum, serratus posterior inferior*	9,10
Malar bone	*masseter*	23,62
Mandible	*digastric, genioglossus, geniohyoid, masseter, mylohyoid*	9,11,13,14
Mastoid process	*digastric, sterno cleido mastoideus*	10,12,13,15
Maxilla		9,11,12

BONE

Muscle attachments
(related to speech)

PAGE

Occipital 10,12,13
  trapezius

Parietal 9,11,12,13

Pubes 9
  external oblique, rectus abdominis

Ribs 9,10
  diaphragm (12th rib), external oblique (lower eight ribs), intercostals -
  internal and external - (all ribs), internal oblique (lower six ribs),
  levatores castarum (all ribs), pectoralis major (5th rib) pectoralis
  minor (3rd through 5th ribs), quadratus lumborum (12th rib), rectus
  abdominis (5th through 7th ribs), scalene (1st and 2nd ribs), serratus
  magnus anterior (first nine ribs), serratus posterior inferior (lower
  four ribs), serratus posterior superior (2nd through 5th ribs), thoracic
  transverse (first five ribs).

Sacrum 10
  latissimus dorsi

Scapula 9,10
  levator scapulae, omohyoid (loop), pectoralis minor, rhomboid, ser-
  ratus magnus anterior, trapezius

Sphenoid 11,12,13
  tensor palati

Sternum 9
  diaphragm, pectoralis major, rectus abdominus, sternohyoid, sterno-
  thyroid, thoracic transverse

Styloid process 12,13,14,15
  stylohyoid

Temporal bone 11
  levator palati

Thoracic vertebrae 10
  latissimus dorsi, levatores costarum, rhomboids, serratus posterior
  inferior, serratus posterior superior, trapezius

Turbinates...11,13,14

Zygomatic arch 9,11

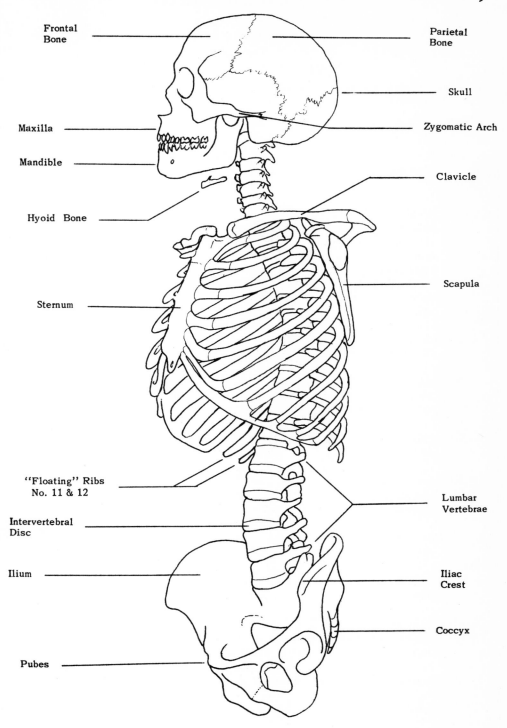

Frontal Bone

Parietal Bone

Skull

Zygomatic Arch

Maxilla

Mandible

Hyoid Bone

Clavicle

Sternum

Scapula

"Floating" Ribs No. 11 & 12

Lumbar Vertebrae

Intervertebral Disc

Ilium

Iliac Crest

Coccyx

Pubes

Fig. 3.

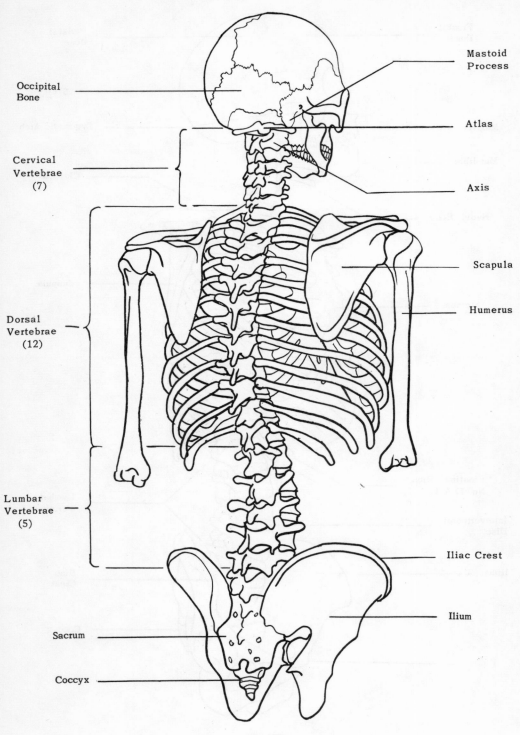

Occipital Bone

Mastoid Process

Cervical Vertebrae (7)

Atlas

Axis

Scapula

Humerus

Dorsal Vertebrae (12)

Lumbar Vertebrae (5)

Iliac Crest

Ilium

Sacrum

Coccyx

Fig. 4.

SKULL

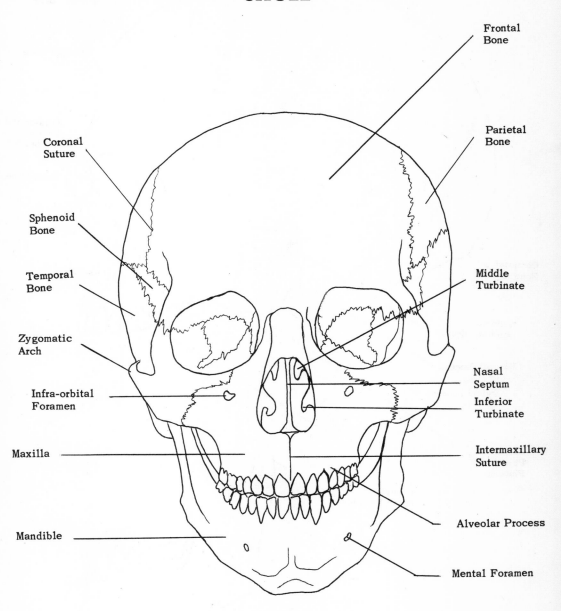

Frontal
Bone

Parietal
Bone

Coronal
Suture

Sphenoid
Bone

Temporal
Bone

Zygomatic
Arch

Infra-orbital
Foramen

Maxilla

Mandible

Middle
Turbinate

Nasal
Septum

Inferior
Turbinate

Intermaxillary
Suture

Alveolar Process

Mental Foramen

Fig. 5.

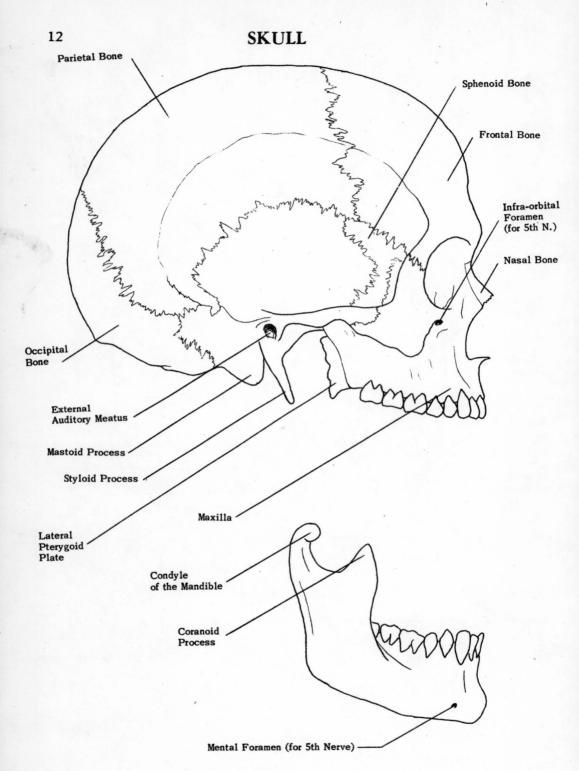

Parietal Bone

Sphenoid Bone

Frontal Bone

Infra-orbital
Foramen
(for 5th N.)

Nasal Bone

Occipital
Bone

External
Auditory Meatus

Mastoid Process

Styloid Process

Maxilla

Lateral
Pterygoid
Plate

Condyle
of the Mandible

Coranoid
Process

Mental Foramen (for 5th Nerve)

Fig. 6.

REAR VIEW, WITH SKULL TILTED FOREWARD

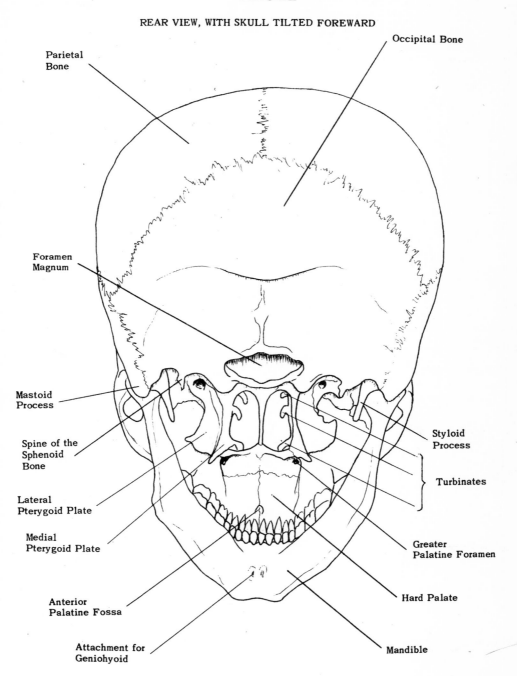

Parietal
Bone

Occipital Bone

Foramen
Magnum

Mastoid
Process

Spine of the
Sphenoid
Bone

Lateral
Pterygoid Plate

Medial
Pterygoid Plate

Anterior
Palatine Fossa

Attachment for
Geniohyoid

Styloid
Process

Turbinates

Greater
Palatine Foramen

Hard Palate

Mandible

Fig. 7.

SKULL

CROSS SECTION

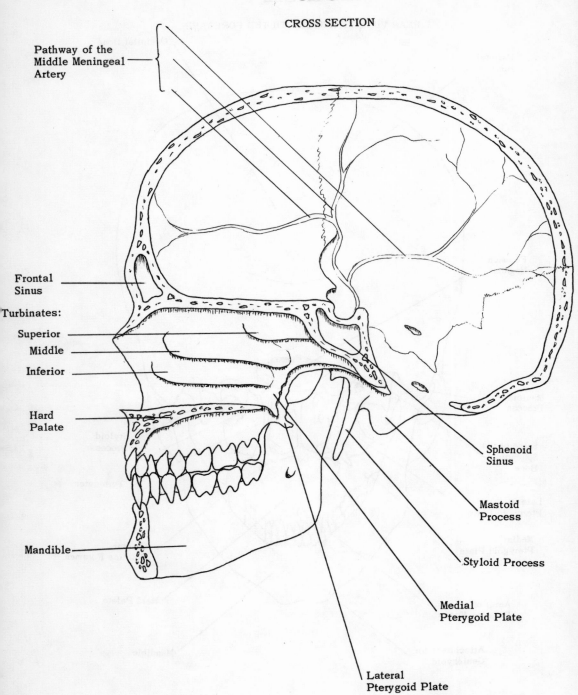

Pathway of the
Middle Meningeal
Artery

Frontal
Sinus

Turbinates:

Superior

Middle

Inferior

Hard
Palate

Mandible

Sphenoid
Sinus

Mastoid
Process

Styloid Process

Medial
Pterygoid Plate

Lateral
Pterygoid Plate

Fig. 8.

SKULL

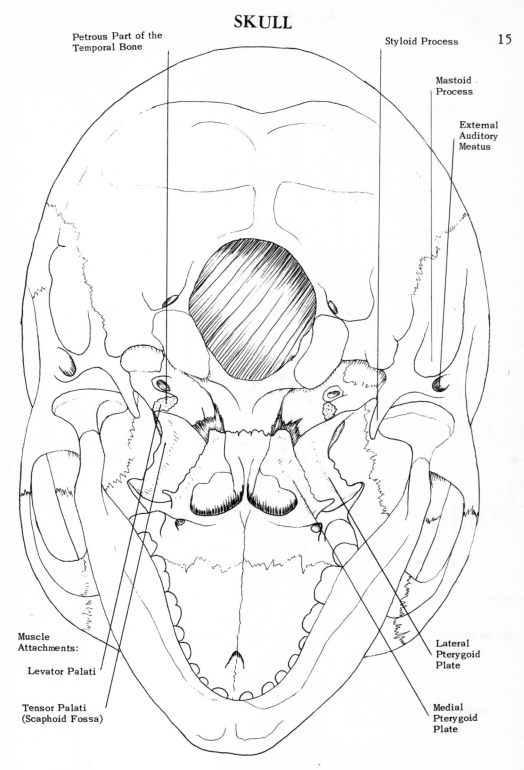

Petrous Part of the
Temporal Bone

Styloid Process

Mastoid
Process

External
Auditory
Meatus

Muscle
Attachments:

Levator Palati

Tensor Palati
(Scaphoid Fossa)

Lateral
Pterygoid
Plate

Medial
Pterygoid
Plate

Fig. 9.

SKULL

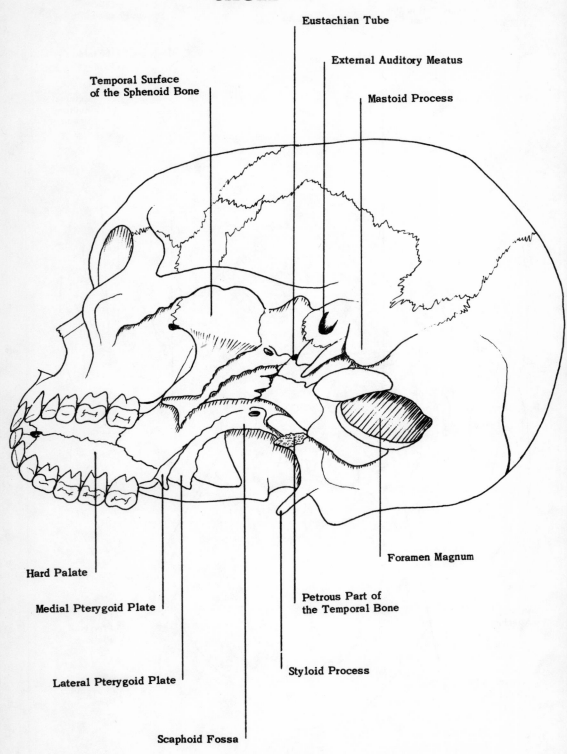

Eustachian Tube

External Auditory Meatus

Mastoid Process

Temporal Surface
of the Sphenoid Bone

Foramen Magnum

Hard Palate

Medial Pterygoid Plate

Petrous Part of
the Temporal Bone

Lateral Pterygoid Plate

Styloid Process

Scaphoid Fossa

Fig. 10.

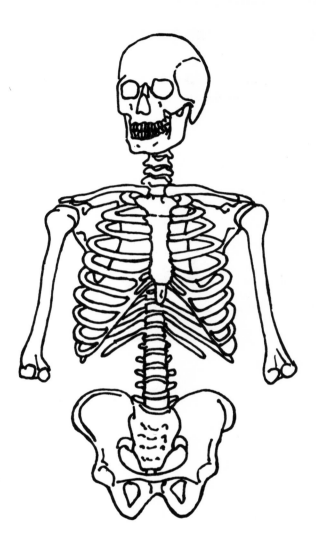

Fig. 11. The Skeleton

Exercise 1. Shade in and label the following muscle attachment areas:

1. Iliac crest
2. Mastoid process
3. Floating ribs
4. Scapula
5. Lumbar vertebrae

6. Sternum
7. Clavicle
8. Cervical vertebrae
9. Humerus
10. Pubes

THE SKELETON

EXERCISE 2 - Most bones of the skeleton have at least two attachments to other bones. Name the attachments to the following bones.

1. ATLAS _____ _____

2. SCAPULA _____ _____

3. LUMBAR VERTEBRAE _____ _____

4. RIBS (1-10) _____ _____

5. CLAVICLE _____ _____

6. STERNUM _____ _____

7. CERVICAL VERTEBRAE _____ _____

8. PARIETAL BONE _____

9. SACRUM _____ _____ _____

10. SPHENOID BONE _____ _____ _____

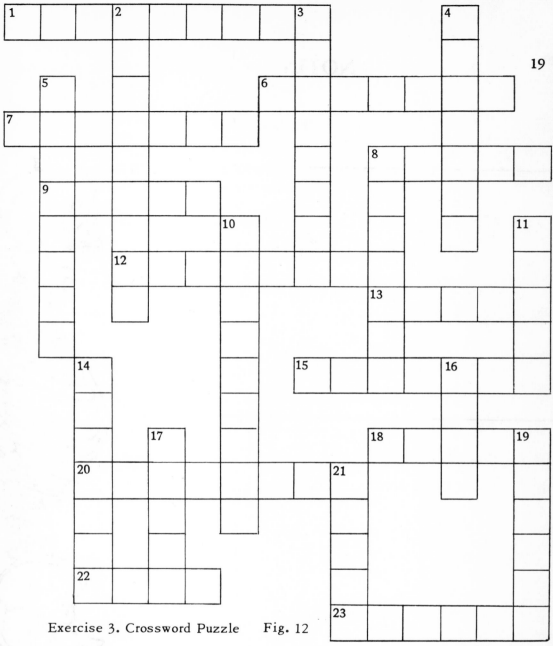

Exercise 3. Crossword Puzzle   Fig. 12

Across:

1. An arch on the skull
6. Front of the skull
7. Upper jaw
8. Head bone
9. Hip bone
12. Base for the upper teeth
13. Refers to the nose
15. Upper arm
18. Front of the ilium
20. Refers to the chest
22. Divider for the vertebrae
23. Number of ribs

Down:

2. Posterior part of the skull
3. Neck vertebrae
4. Shoulder bone
5. Side of the skull
8. Front of the chest
10. Bones of the spine
11. Top vertebrae
14. Lower side of the skull
16. Bones of the thorax
17. Units of the skeleton
19. Seam between skull bones
21. Upper edge of the ilium

NOTES

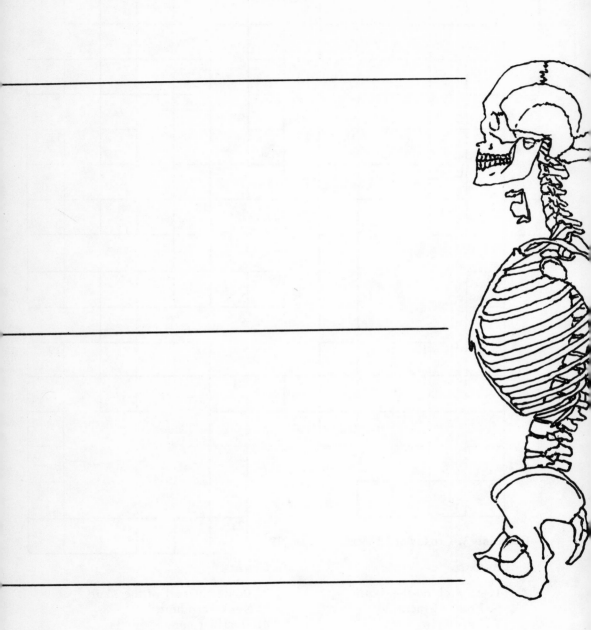

Fig. 13.

INHALATION

In order to inhale, the *diaphragm* must push the stomach down from the rib cage, and the ribs must be pulled upward and outward at the front and sides. This is accomplished by the *diaphragm* muscle itself, as well as by the muscles which attach primarily to the ribs and to the bones of the head, neck, and shoulders. An exception is the *quadratus lumborum,* which appears to have a stabilizing influence by holding the lower ribs and back firmly during deep inhalation.

MUSCLES OF INHALATION

MUSCLE	LOCATION	PAGE
1. DIAPHRAGM: Sternum, costal cartilages, lumber vertebrae, 12th rib		22,27
2. INTERCOSTALS: Between all ribs		25
3. LEVATOR SCAPULAE: Upper four cervical vertebrae to scapula		31
4. LEVATORES COSTARUM: Side of each vertebrae to top of next lowest rib		25
5. PECTORALIS MAJOR: Upper outside of humerous to side of sternum and to clavicle and 6th rib		22
6. PECTORALIS MINOR: Coracoid process of scapula to 3rd, 4th, and 5th rib		22
7. QUADRATUS LUMBORUM: Iliac crest to lumbar vertebrae and 12th rib		22,26
8. RHOMBOIDEUS MAJOR: 2nd through 5th thoracic vertebrae to scapula		31
9. RHOMBOIDEUS MINOR: 7th cervical and 1st thoracic vertebrae to scapula		31
10. SCALENE: Cervical vertebrae to 1st and 2nd rib		24,26
11. SERRATUS MAGNUS ANTERIOR: Inner surface of scapula to first nine ribs		29
12. SERRATUS POSTERIOR SUPERIOR: 7th cervical and first three thoracic vertebrae to the 2nd through 5th ribs		25
13. STERNO CLEIDO MASTOIDEUS: Mastoid process to sternum and clavicle		23
14. TRAPEZIUS: Base of the skull, spine of the scapula to 12th thoracic vertebrae		23,26

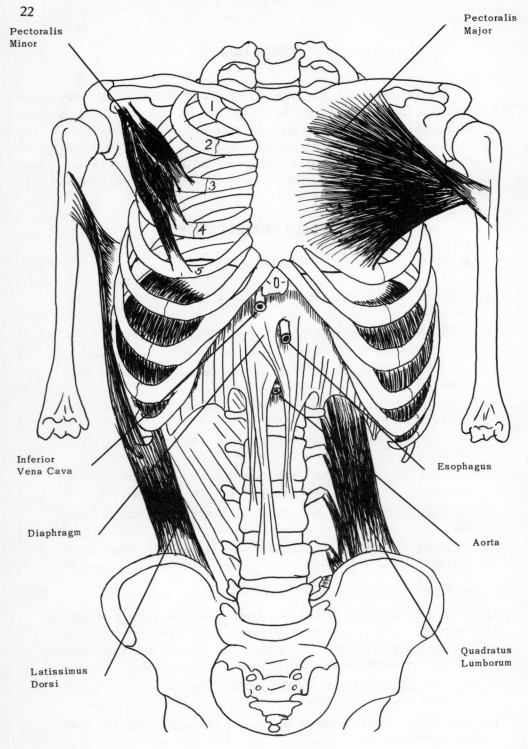

Pectoralis
Minor

Pectoralis
Major

Inferior
Vena Cava

Esophagus

Diaphragm

Aorta

Latissimus
Dorsi

Quadratus
Lumborum

Fig. 14.

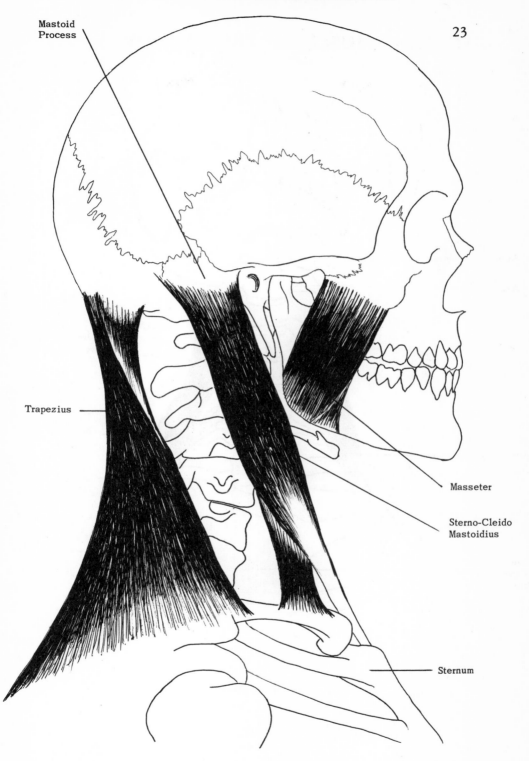

Mastoid
Process

Trapezius

Masseter

Sterno-Cleido
Mastoidius

Sternum

Fig. 15.

SCALENE MUSCLES: FRONT VIEW

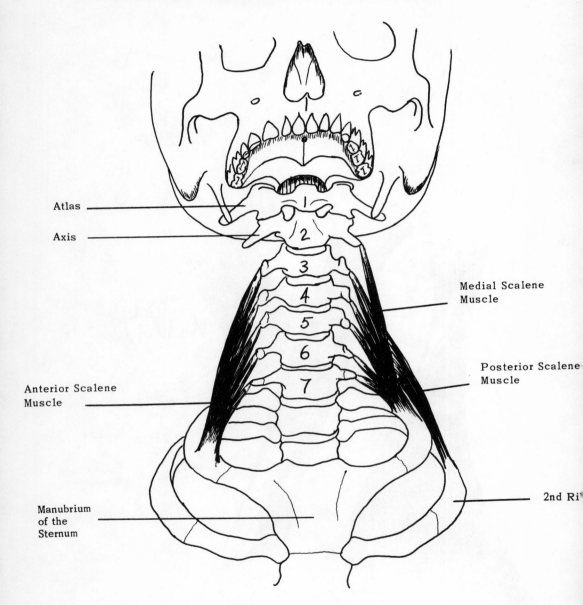

Atlas

Axis

Anterior Scalene
Muscle

Manubrium
of the
Sternum

Medial Scalene
Muscle

Posterior Scalene
Muscle

2nd Rib

Lower jaw is removed.

Fig. 16.

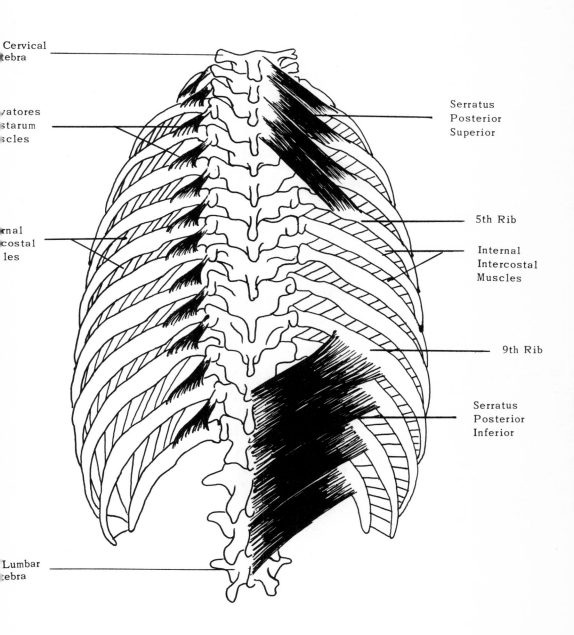

Cervical
tebra

vatores
starum
scles

rnal
costal
les

Lumbar
:ebra

Serratus
Posterior
Superior

5th Rib

Internal
Intercostal
Muscles

9th Rib

Serratus
Posterior
Inferior

Fig. 17.

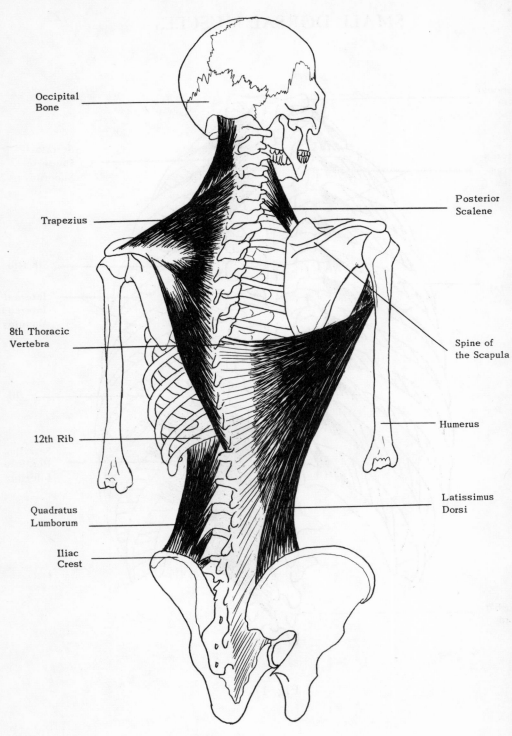

Occipital
Bone

Posterior
Scalene

Trapezius

8th Thoracic
Vertebra

Spine of
the Scapula

12th Rib

Humerus

Quadratus
Lumborum

Latissimus
Dorsi

Iliac
Crest

Fig. 18.

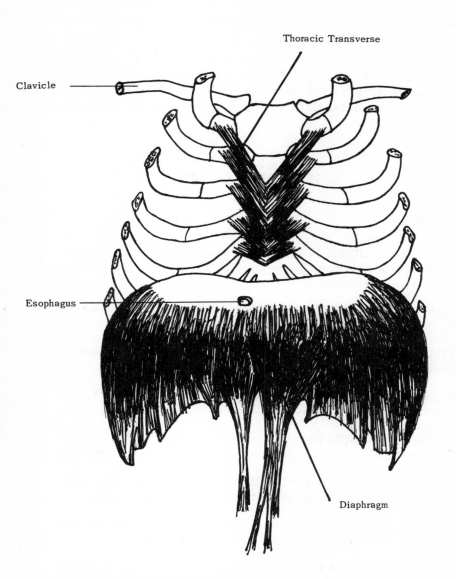

VIEW FROM INSIDE THE RIB CAGE, LOOKING FORWARD

Fig. 19.

EXHALATION

Basically, in order to exhale, one needs simply to relax. When relaxation occurs, the pull of gravity will lower the ribs and the normal tone of the abdominal muscles will cause the stomach to occupy part of the chest cavity. This decrease in lung space will result in a shallow exhalation, which may be sufficient for breathing while at rest. However, in public speaking or physical exertion a deeper breathing is necessary, which requires forced exhalation, employing the rib and abdominal muscles.

MUSCLES OF EXHALATION

MUSCLE	LOCATION	PAGE
1. EXTERNAL OBLIQUE: From the iliac crest to the linea alba and up to the lower eight ribs. It interlocks on the ribs with the serratus anterior		29,30
2. INTERNAL OBLIQUE: From the crest and front of the ilium up to the lower four ribs and the linea alba		31
3. LATISSIMUS DORSI: From the last six thoracic vertebrae, lumbar vertebrae, sacrum, and iliac crest up to the humerus		22,26
4. QUADRATUS LUMBORUM: From the iliac crest up to the lumbar vertebrae and 12th rib		22,26
5. RECTUS ABDOMINUS: From the pubis up to the 5th, 6th, and 7th rib and sternum		30
6. SERRATUS POSTERIOR INFERIOR: 11th and 12th thoracic vertebrae, and 1st and 2nd lumbar vertebrae up to the four lower ribs		25
7. THORACIC TRANSVERSE: From the lower sternum up to the first four ribs. It is located on the inner surface of the rib cage		27,29
8. TRANSVERSE ABDOMINIS: From the front of the iliac crest, lumbar vertebrae, lower two ribs, and costal cartilage to the linea alba. It is covered by the internal oblique		30,31

SERRATUS MAGNUS & EXTERNAL OBLIQUE

THESE TWO MUSCLES MEET AT THE 5TH, 6TH, 7TH, 8TH, AND 9TH RIBS.

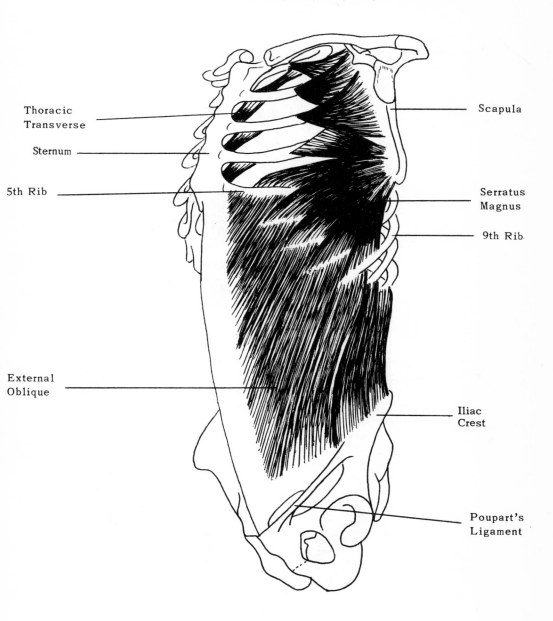

Thoracic
Transverse

Sternum

5th Rib

External
Oblique

Scapula

Serratus
Magnus

9th Rib

Iliac
Crest

Poupart's
Ligament

Fig. 20

ABDOMINAL MUSCLES

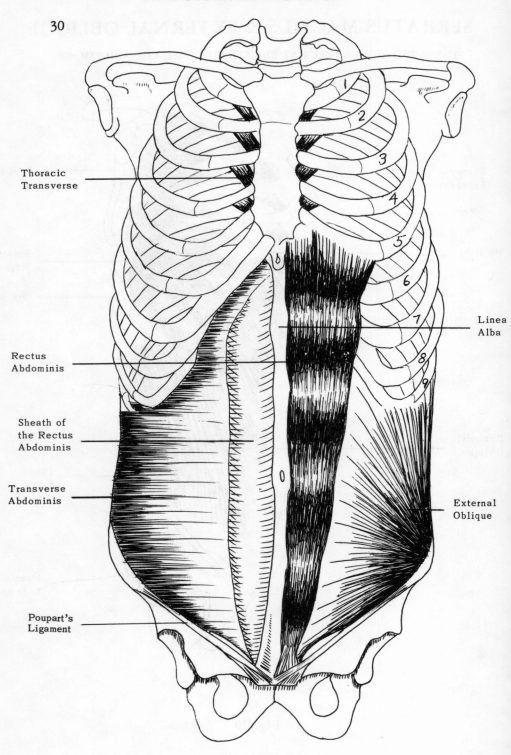

Thoracic Transverse

Rectus Abdominis

Sheath of the Rectus Abdominis

Transverse Abdominis

Poupart's Ligament

Linea Alba

External Oblique

Fig. 21.

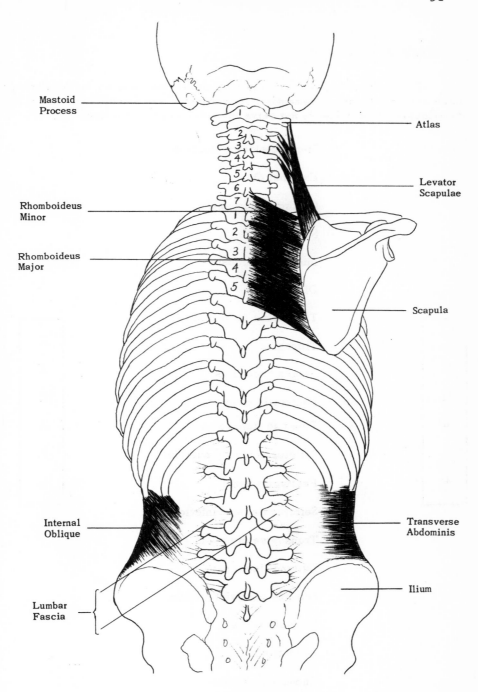

Mastoid
Process

Atlas

Levator
Scapulae

Rhomboideus
Minor

Rhomboideus
Major

Scapula

Internal
Oblique

Transverse
Abdominis

Ilium

Lumbar
Fascia

Fig. 22.

EXERCISE 4 - Respiration.

Draw connecting lines to show which are the muscles for inhalation and which are for exhalation. Remember, some muscles serve dual functions. A few of the muscles listed below do not serve the function of respiration.

Sterno-cleido-mastoideus

External oblique

Quadratus lumborum

Scalene

Internal intercostals

Digastric

Transverse abdominis

Trapezius

Rectus abdominis

Pectoralis minor

Thoracic transverse

Serratus posterior superior

Pectoralis minor

Serratus magnus anterior

Transverse arytenoid

External intercostals

Serratus posterior inferior

Latissimus dorsi

Levator scapulae

Rhomboideus minor

I
N
H
A
L
E

E
X
H
A
L
E

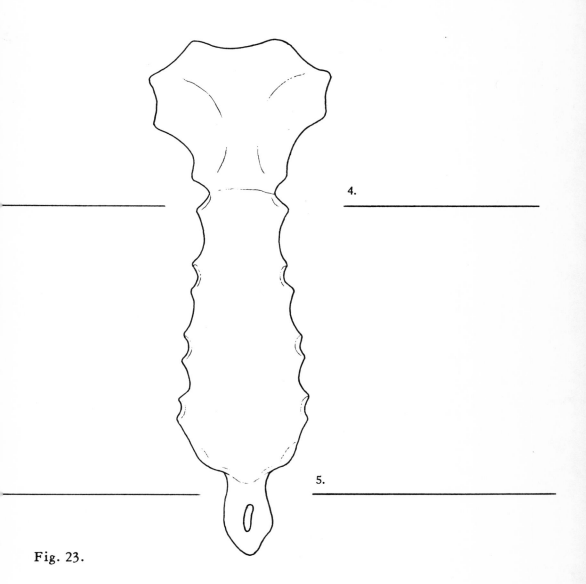

4.

5.

Fig. 23.

Exercise 5. Respiration. There are at least five muscles which attach to the sternum. Write the names of these muscles on the lines below and draw a connecting line to the sternum, showing their approximate location. Shade in the parts of the sternum to show the approximate areas of muscle attachment.

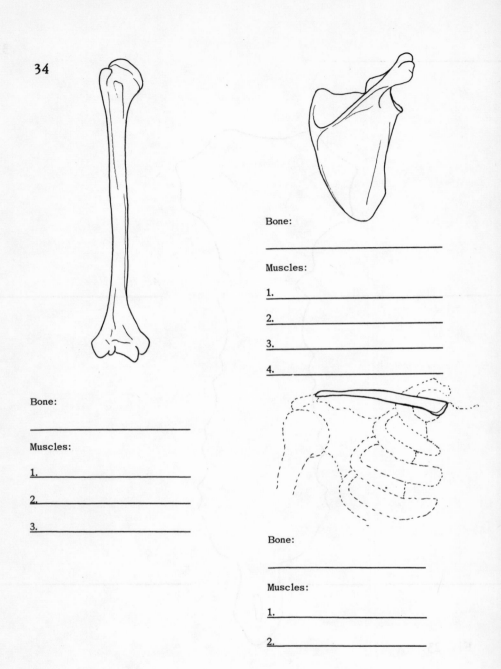

34

Bone:

_____

Muscles:

1._____

2._____

3._____

Bone:

_____

Muscles:

1._____

2._____

3._____

4._____

Bone:

_____

Muscles:

1._____

2._____

Fig. 24.

Exercise 6. Respiration. Label the following bones and list the indicated number of breathing muscles attached to each one.

EXERCISE 7 - Respiration.

Match the muscles with their functions: (Note: Some muscles have more than one function.)

1. EXTERNAL OBLIQUE _____

2. INTERNAL OBLIQUE _____

3. LEVATORES COSTARUM _____

4. PECTORALIS MINOR _____

5. QUADRATUS LUMBORUM _____

6. RECTUS ABDOMINIS _____

7. SCALENE _____

8. SERRATUS MAGNUS ANTERIOR _____

9. SERRATUS POSTERIOR INFERIOR _____

10. SERRATUS POSTERIOR SUPERIOR _____

11. STERNO CLEIDO MASTOIDIUS _____

12. THORACIC TRANSVERSE _____

13. TRANSVERSE ABDOMINIS _____

A. Raises ribs from the back   D. Pulls abdomen inward

B. Raises ribs from the front   E. Pulls ribs down in back

C. Raises ribs from the side   F. Pulls ribs down in front

EXERCISE 8 - Respiration

1. Describe the inhale process.

a. To push the stomach down and forward:

Muscle   Attachments   Specific Function

_____

b. To raise the rib cage upward and forward:

Muscle   Attachments   Specific Function

_____

_____

_____

_____

_____

_____

2. Describe the forced exhale process.

a. To lower and flatten the rib cage:

Muscle   Attachments   Specific Function

_____

_____

_____

_____

b. To force the stomach in and upward:

Muscle   Attachments   Specific Function

_____

_____

_____

_____

EXERCISE 9 - Phonation.

Give the names and functions of the parts of the larynx:

NAME	FUNCTION

1. _____ _____

2. _____ _____

3. _____ _____

4. _____ _____

5. _____ _____

6. _____ _____

7. What is the primary muscle in controlling pitch? _____

_____

8. What is the primary muscle in drawing the vocal cords together? _____

_____

9. What part of the larynx covers the glottis during swallowing? _____

_____

10. Name the smallest cartilage of the larynx group. _____

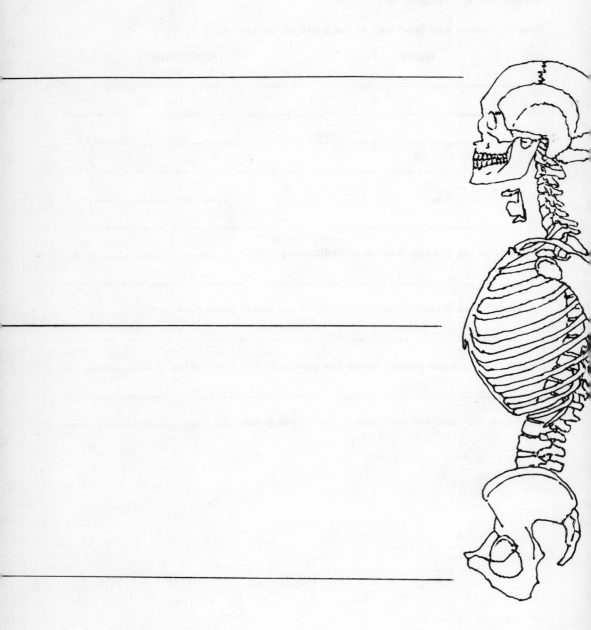

Fig. 36.

4

ARTICULATION

THE ARTICULATION PROCESS

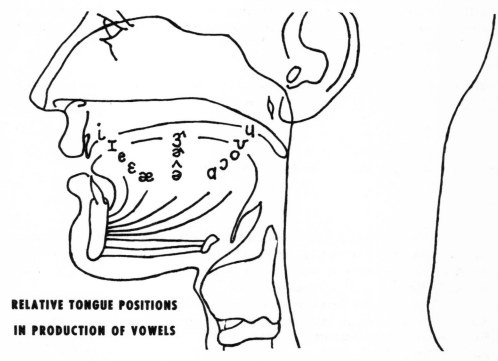

RELATIVE TONGUE POSITIONS

IN PRODUCTION OF VOWELS

Fig. 37. Articulation of the Vowels. Generally speaking, half the vowels are made by raising the front of the tongue and half are made by raising it in the back. Of the remaining vowels, the ⌈ʌ⌉ and ⌈ə⌉ are made with the tongue held comparatively low and flat, while the ⌈ɝ⌉ and ⌈ɚ⌉ are made with the tongue raised both in front and back.

When the front of the tongue is raised in the production of vowels the lips are also retracted at the corners, as in the ⌈i⌉ sound. For this reason, we appear to be smiling when we say *cheese*. When the tongue is raised for back vowels the lips are also protruded, as in the ⌈u⌉.

The approximate location of the tongue for vowels is shown in the accompanying diagram.

ARTICULATION OF THE CONSONANTS

The consonants do not follow a set and consecutive pattern in their arrangement as well as do the vowels. For example, the [l, n, t] and [d] are all made with the tongue tip touching the same spot on the roof of the mouth. Their identities, therefore, are established not so much by the tongue position but by the manner in which the air stream is emitted. These four sounds would thus be phonetically classified as lateral, nasal, unvoiced plosive, and voiced plosive, respectively. From a purely anatomic point of view, however, a visualization of the relative tongue position will be sufficient for an understanding of the action of the muscles of articulation. The following classification of the consonants indicates these tongue positions:

Tongue raised toward front	Tongue raised centrally	Tongue raised toward back
θ ð ʃ ʒ n d t l j	r	g k ŋ w
s z tʃ dʒ r		

Tongue in neutral position

v f p b h m

Although the [h] is classified here in the neutral position, it actually assumes the position of the vowel which it precedes in the word. For example, in the words *he* and *who* the tongue formation for the [h] would resemble the [i] and [u], respectively.

The complete function of all muscles involved during the articulation of one word is so intricate as to defy precise description. However, for a general understanding of this process certain basic elements are sufficiently helpful. The foremost of these is the relationship of the tongue's movement with that of the hyoid bone. Since a large portion of the *base of the tongue* is attached to the upper surface of the *hyoid bone*, many of the tongue movements in articulation are accompanied by similar movements of the hyoid bone. This may be observed by touching the fingers to the sides of the hyoid bone while repeating the [l] sound. Muscles which move the hyoid bone thus also aid in the movements of the tongue.

The tip of the tongue appears to be actuated by the separate movements of the superior and inferior longitudinal muscles. This action may be visualized as being analogous to that of a folded sheet of paper. When the upper surface is pulled back, the tip tends to curl upward.

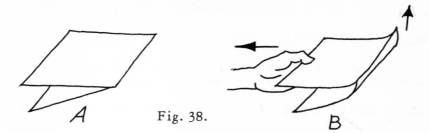

Fig. 38.

Throughout the process of articulation of the front and back tongue sounds, the tongue is characteristically lowered at the opposite end from which it is raised. Thus, for the [k] sound the tongue is raised in the back and lowered in the front. With the [l] sound the tongue is raised in the front and lowered in the back. Diagramatic presentations of tongue positions in the production of speech sounds may be found in texts such as those by Kantner and West[1] and Carrell and Tiffany.[2]

Since the tongue itself is composed almost entirely of muscle, a sluggish tongue can often be made more flexible for articulation after about six weeks of regular exercises. However, the ability to curl the sides of the tongue is a hereditary characteristic and cannot be trained in most cases.

[1]Kantner, C. E., and West, R.: *Phonetics*, Rev. Ed. New York, Harper, 1960.
[2]Carrell, J., and Tiffany, W. R.: *Phonetics*. New York, McGraw-Hill, 1960.

MUSCLES OF THE TONGUE

MUSCLE	LOCATION	PAGE
1. GENIOGLOSSUS: From the inner-front of the mandible, fanning backward and upward to the extent of the tongue's surface		59,68
2. LONGITUDINALIS LINGUAE INFERIOR: Runs the length of the lower half of the tongue blade		59
3. LONGITUDINALIS LINGUAE SUPERIOR: Runs the length of the upper half of the tongue blade		59
4. TRANSVERSUS LINGUAE: Runs between the two sides of the tongue for the length of the tongue blade		59
5. VERTICALIS LINGUAE: Runs vertically within the tongue for the length of the blade		59

MUSCLES OF THE HYOID BONE

MUSCLE	LOCATION	PAGE
1. DIGASTRIC: Appears as two muscled joined by a central tendon. Entire muscle extends from the mastoid process through a loop on the side of the hyoid bone, and forward to the inside-front of the mandible		62
2. GENIOHYOID: Front of the hyoid bone to the inside-front of the mandible		60
3. HYOGLOSSUS: Side of the hyoid bone to the side of the tongue		60
4. MYLOHYOID: Lower inside surface of the front of the mandible to the body of the hyoid bone		61
5. OMOHYOID: Upper border of the scapula through a loop from the clavicle to the body of the hyoid bone		61,62
6. STERNOHYOID: Sternum and clavicle to the front-side of the hyoid bone		60,61
7. STYLOHYOID: Styloid process to the upper-side of the hyoid bone		68
8. THYROHYOID: Continues from the sternothyroid. From the side of the thyroid cartilage to the side of the hyoid bone		68

MUSCLES OF THE TONGUE

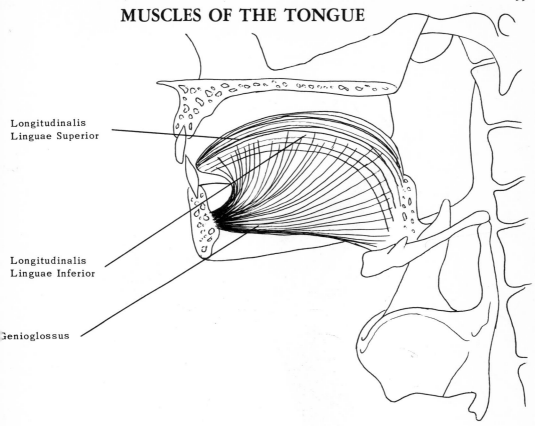

Longitudinalis
Linguae Superior

Longitudinalis
Linguae Inferior

Genioglossus

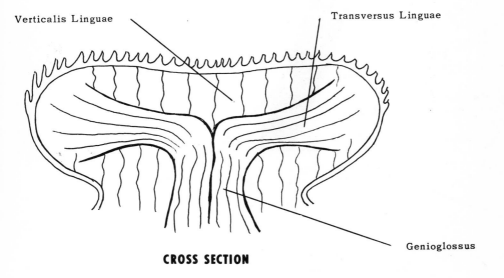

Verticalis Linguae

Transversus Linguae

Genioglossus

CROSS SECTION

Fig. 39.

MUSCLES OF ARTICULATION

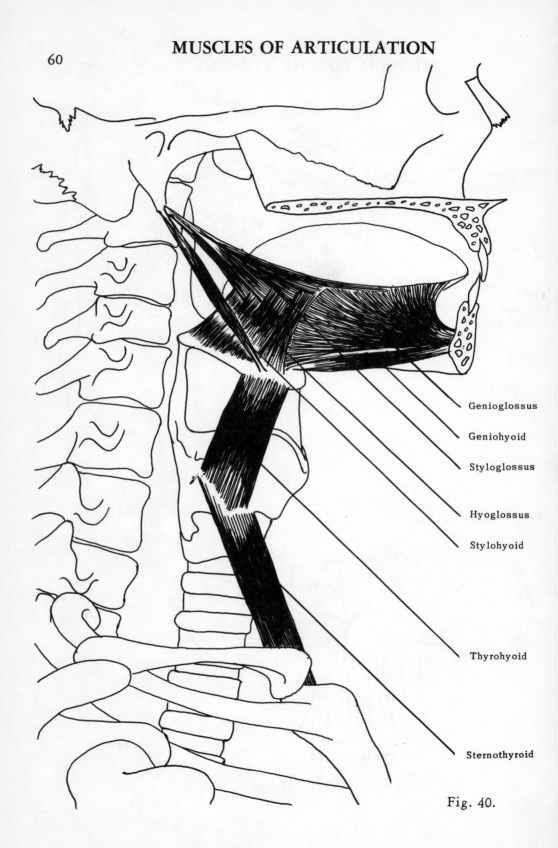

Genioglossus

Geniohyoid

Styloglossus

Hyoglossus

Stylohyoid

Thyrohyoid

Sternothyroid

Fig. 40.

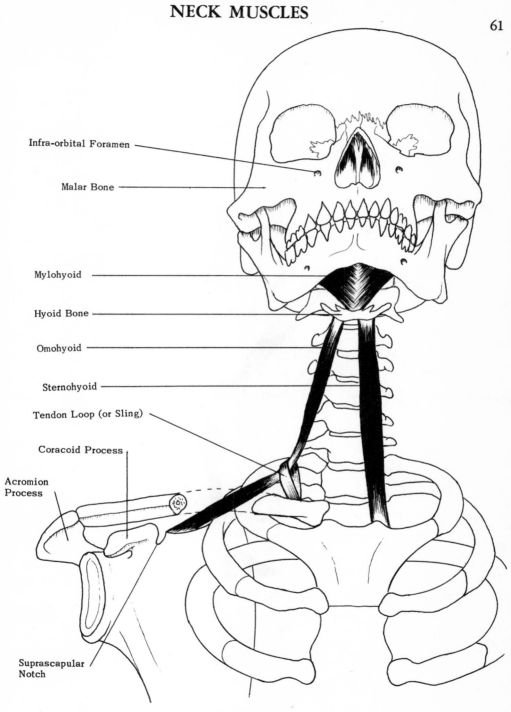

Infra-orbital Foramen

Malar Bone

Mylohyoid

Hyoid Bone

Omohyoid

Sternohyoid

Tendon Loop (or Sling)

Coracoid Process

Acromion
Process

Suprascapular
Notch

Fig. 41.

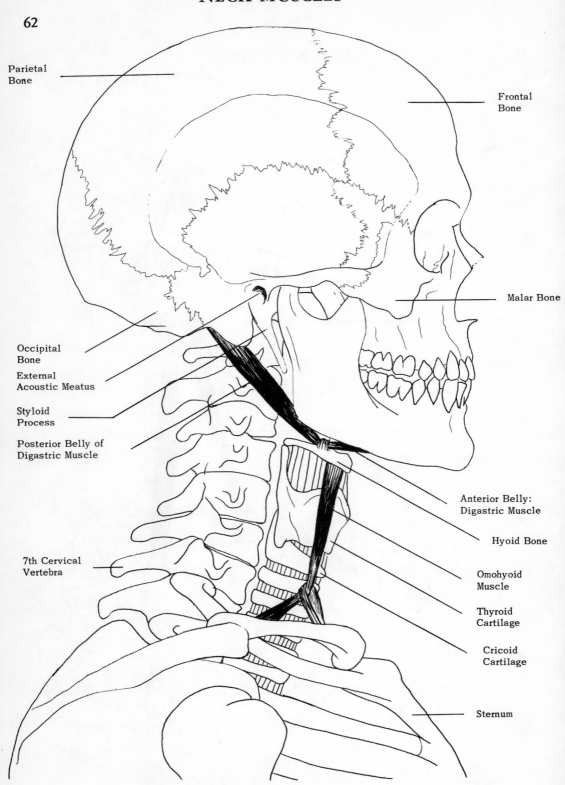

Parietal
Bone

Frontal
Bone

Malar Bone

Occipital
Bone

External
Acoustic Meatus

Styloid
Process

Posterior Belly of
Digastric Muscle

Anterior Belly:
Digastric Muscle

Hyoid Bone

Omohyoid
Muscle

Thyroid
Cartilage

Cricoid
Cartilage

7th Cervical
Vertebra

Sternum

Fig. 42.

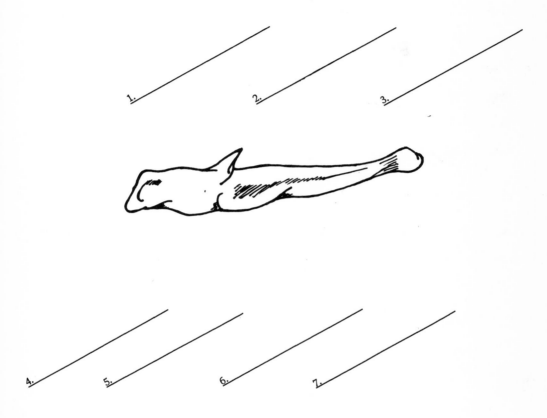

Fig. 43.

Exercise 10. Articulation. There are at least seven muscles of articulation which attach to the hyoid bone. Write the names of these muscles on the lines below and draw a connecting line to the hyoid bone, showing their approximate location. Shade in the parts of the bone to show the approximate areas of muscle attachment.

EXERCISE 11 - Articulation

The following muscles are attached to the hyoid bone. Give the other attachment and functions of each.

digastric _____

ohmohyoid _____

stylohyoid _____

hyoglossus _____

thyrohyoid _____

sternohyoid _____

....

Which of the following muscles are activated to raise the front of the tongue?

_____ mylohyoid

_____ longitudinalis lingual superior

_____ sternohyoid

_____ palato glossus

_____ transverse arytenoid

_____ diaphram

_____ longitudinalis lingual inferior

_____ levator palati

_____ rectus abdominis

NOTES

_____

_____

_____

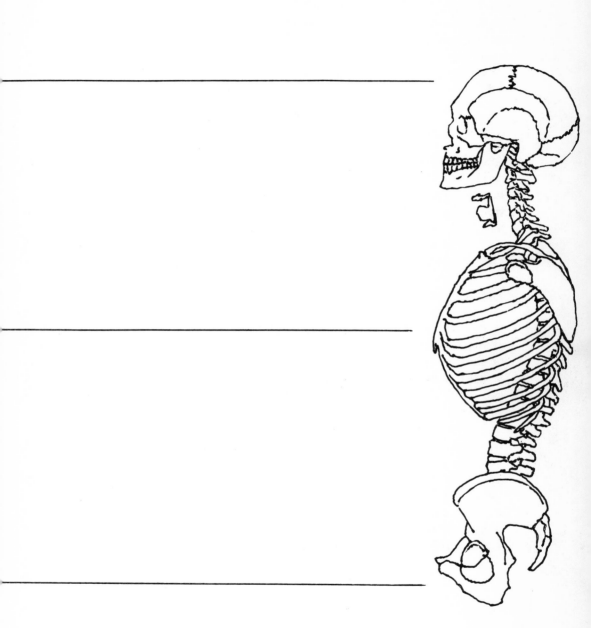

Fig. 44.

5

RESONANCE

The musician can still blow a tune on a mouthpiece after he removes it from the trumpet, but the tone has no musical quality. The curved tubes in the trumpet provide the *resonators*. In the human voice, the larynx would make a raspy inharmonious noise if it were not for the throat, mouth, and nose, which provide the majority of the resonance.

Although in most speakers the nasal cavity is never completely closed, some sounds receive more nasal resonance than others. The three sounds which are emitted through the nose rather than the mouth are the ⌈m , n⌉ and ⌈ŋ⌉.

Since some nasal resonance is present in nearly all speech sounds it is more realistic to consider degree of nasality rather than presence or absence of this quality in the speaking voice. In most instances the ratio of the two air streams emitted through the nose and the mouth is more important than the nasal opening *per se*. Many cases of excessive nasality can thus be improved through practice in opening the mouth wider during speech.

Sounds which tend to obstruct the air stream as it comes through the mouth are also apt to have some nasal quality. Among these sounds are the ⌈l, ʒ⌉ and ⌈u⌉.

In normal speech increased nasalization is achieved by lowering the soft palate. This is done primarily by the action of the *palatoglossus*. For non-nasal sounds, the palate is held in the raised position by *levator palati*. Additional closure of the nasopharynx is often aided by the *superior constrictor*, which surrounds the pharyngeal wall.

MUSCLES OF THE PALATE AND PHARYNX

MUSCLE   **LOCATION**   **PAGE**

MUSCLES OF THE PHARYNX AND NECK

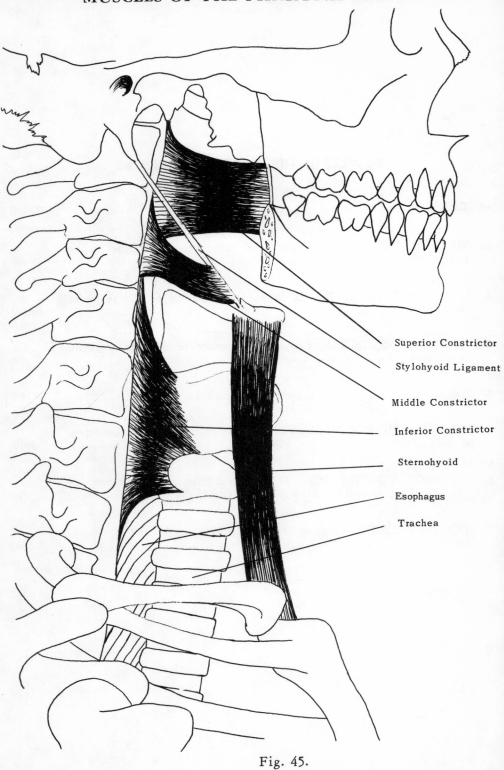

Superior Constrictor

Stylohyoid Ligament

Middle Constrictor

Inferior Constrictor

Sternohyoid

Esophagus

Trachea

Fig. 45.

MUSCLES OF THE PALATE

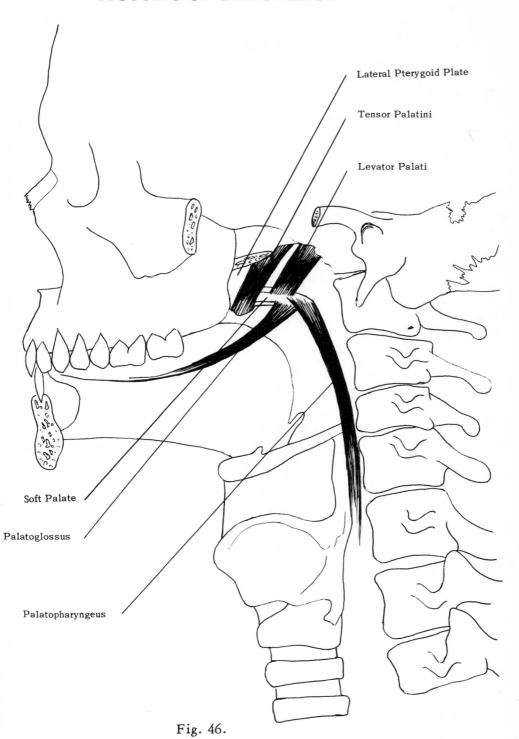

Lateral Pterygoid Plate

Tensor Palatini

Levator Palati

Soft Palate

Palatoglossus

Palatopharyngeus

Fig. 46.

MUSCLES OF THE PALATE AND PHARYNX

REAR VIEW

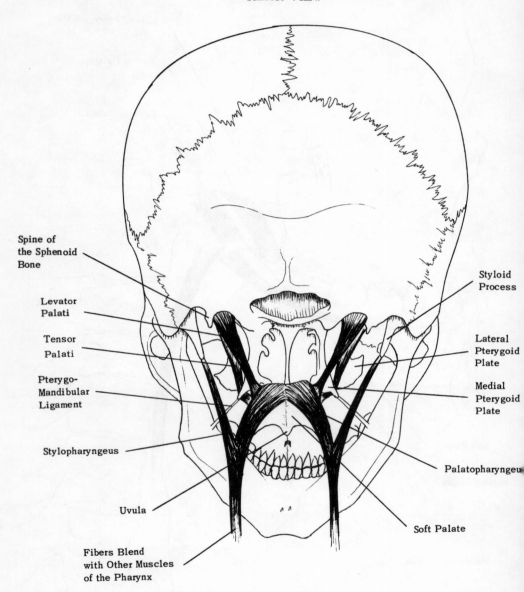

Spine of
the Sphenoid
Bone

Levator
Palati

Tensor
Palati

Pterygo-
Mandibular
Ligament

Stylopharyngeus

Uvula

Fibers Blend
with Other Muscles
of the Pharynx

Styloid
Process

Lateral
Pterygoid
Plate

Medial
Pterygoid
Plate

Palatopharyngeu

Soft Palate

Fig. 47.

EXERCISE 12 - Articulation and Resonance

The ___l___ sound $\left\{ \begin{matrix} \text{is} \\ \text{is not} \end{matrix} \right\}$ phonated.

Muscles involved in phonation are:

	Muscle	Attachments	Action
1.			
2.			
3.			
4.			
5.			

The ___l___ sound has a $\left\{ \begin{matrix} \text{front} \\ \text{middle} \\ \text{neutral} \\ \text{back} \end{matrix} \right\}$ tongue position.

Muscles involved for this articulation are:

	Muscle	Attachments	Action
1.			
2.			
3.			
4.			

The ___l___ sound $\left\{ \begin{matrix} \text{is} \\ \text{is not} \end{matrix} \right\}$ nasalized.

Muscles which $\left\{ \begin{matrix} \text{raise} \\ \text{lower} \end{matrix} \right\}$ the palate are:

	Muscle	Attachments	Action
1.			
2.			

EXERCISE 13 - Articulation and Resonance

The ___ŋ___ sound $\begin{Bmatrix} is \\ is\ not \end{Bmatrix}$ phonated.

Muscles involved in phonation are:

	Muscle	Attachments	Action
1.			
2.			
3.			
4.			
5.			

The ___ŋ___ sound is a $\begin{Bmatrix} front \\ middle \\ neutral \\ back \end{Bmatrix}$ tongue position.

Muscles involved for this articulation are:

	Muscle	Attachments	Action
1.			
2.			
3.			
4.			

The ___ŋ___ sound $\begin{Bmatrix} is \\ is\ not \end{Bmatrix}$ nasalized.

Muscles which $\begin{Bmatrix} raise \\ lower \end{Bmatrix}$ the palate are:

	Muscle	Attachments	Action
1.			
2.			

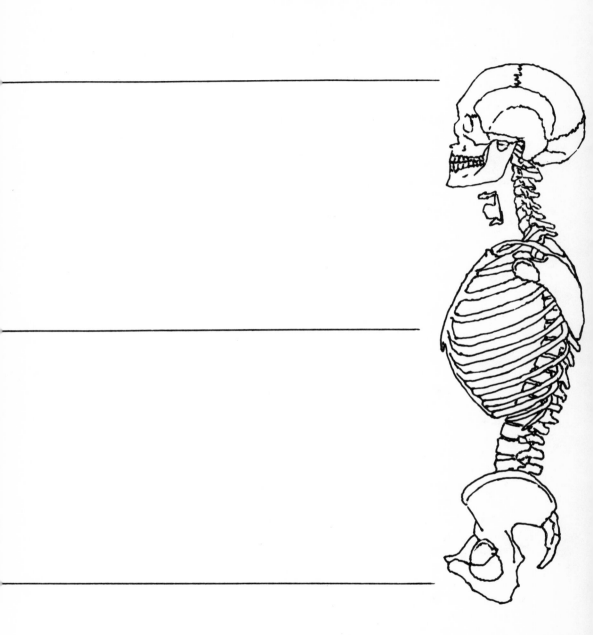

Fig. 48.

6

THE ANATOMY OF THE EAR

In comparing the anatomical structures for speech with those for hearing, one is struck by the greater preponderance of neurological data concerning the auditory system.

Unlike speech, the neurophysiology of hearing can realistically be studied in laboratory animals.

Most of the information on the auditory pathway has been obtained from the cat rather than from the human, and for this reason we can thank the common alley cat for his contributions toward the understanding of human disorders such as Meniere's syndrome, acoustic trauma, and drug toxicity.

THE OUTER EAR

The outer ear or *pinna* is more important to cosmetic appearance than to hearing, although a congenitally malformed ear is often the first clue to an undeveloped ear canal or middle ear structure. A congenitally closed ear canal is said to have *atresia,* which can usually be treated surgically.

The *ear canal* itself serves several purposes: the hairs and wax, or cerumen, along the walls of the canal tend to keep it free of dust and small insects. The recessed structure of the canal shields the ear drum from bumps and scrapes which would otherwise damage its delicate tissue. Finally, the natural resonating frequency of the ear canal, which is about one and one-fourth inches long, lends additional amplification to sounds in the proximity of 3500 Hz.

The *ear drum,* which completely seals the end of the ear canal, has an area of about one-fifth square inch or roughly the top area of the eraser on an ordinary pencil. The area of the eardrum is important in the understanding of the amplification gained as the sound passes through the middle ear. Pressure on the comparatively large area of the eardrum increases in intensity as it is focused on the smaller area of the oval window. The same principle may be seen to operate every time a common thumbtack is used. The entire pressure on the thumb side of the tack is exerted upon the tiny point, enabling it to be pressed easily into the wall.

Scar tissue on the eardrum may produce a stiffness in the vibrating surface. This condition may result in a low frequency hearing loss of from 15 to 35 decibels, depending upon the location and extent of the scar tissue. However, scar tissue from a surgical incision at the extreme perimeter of the eardrum is unlikely to produce any significant impairment.

THE MIDDLE EAR

Under a strong light the first of the ossicles, the *malleus,* may be seen running in a nearly verticle line behind the upper half of the eardrum. Behind the malleus are the *incus* and *stapes,* which terminate the *ossicular chain* at the *oval window.* The three ossicles serve a number of purposes in the hearing system, in addition to the simple transmission of sound. The lever action in the arrangement of the ossicles serves to amplify the sound by the time it reaches the oval window. The ossicles also serve, with assistance from the two middle ear muscles, to protect the ear from loud noise. Finally, as discussed earlier, there is an amplification factor gained through the ossicles as they focus the sound from a large surface on to a smaller one. The sound pressure ratio between the eardrum and oval window has been measured at 15 to 1.

The ossicles are housed in a chamber which comprises the *middle ear.* The most common disorder encountered within the ossicular structure is known as *otosclerosis,* which is the development of a porous bony growth usually around the inco-stapedial joint. Many cases of this type can be helped by surgical removal of the otosclerotic tissue.

The two middle ear muscles, the *tensor tympani* and the *stapedius,* are attached to the ossicles in such a manner that they pull in opposition to each other and are thus able to hold the ossicles in a fixed, rigid position. Up until recently, their function was dismissed as being simply one of protection against loud noise. However, in sudden loud noise, such as hammering or gun shots, this protection is relatively ineffective. The shock wave of a gunshot, for example, has already passed through the ear by the time the middle ear muscles can contract. Since these muscles are also active during relatively quiet sounds, it is conceivable that they may also serve to aid our listening ability.

Another structure located in the middle ear is the *chorda tympani,* a branch of the fifth nerve, which appears like a string running laterally across the back of the eardrum. This sensory nerve is of particular interest because of its vulnerability to damage during middle ear surgery. The postoperative patient in such cases may complain of loss of taste in one side of the tongue. Fortunately, however, most patients adapt to this peculiar sensation after several weeks.

Since the middle ear is an enclosed air chamber, some opening is necessary to allow a pressure equalization of the enclosed air with that

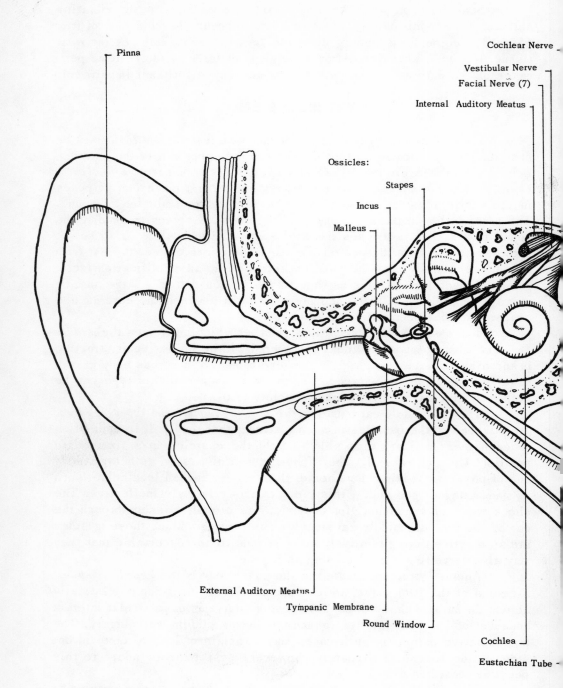

Fig. 49

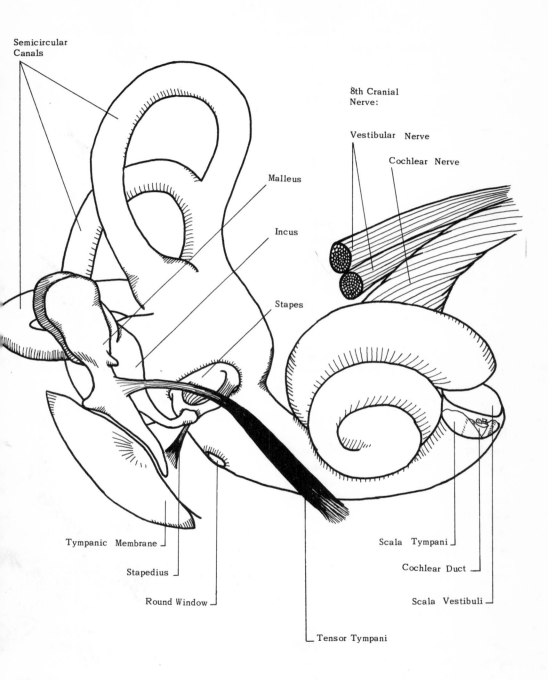

Semicircular
Canals

8th Cranial
Nerve:

Vestibular Nerve

Cochlear Nerve

Malleus

Incus

Stapes

Tympanic Membrane

Stapedius

Round Window

Tensor Tympani

Scala Tympani

Cochlear Duct

Scala Vestibuli

Fig. 50

of the surrounding atmosphere. This purpose is served by the *eustachean tube,* which is usually opened during yawning or swallowing. The opening is accomplished through the action of the *tensor paletini* and the *salpingopharyngeus muscles,* as they stretch the walls of the nasopharynx. During upper respiratory disturbances, such as colds or allergies, the eustachean tube may not be able to open and the resulting difference in air pressures tightens and restricts the movement of the eardrum. This condition is called *otitus media.*

THE INNER EAR

The inner ear consists of the *cochlea,* a structure resembling a snail shell, which houses the *hair cells,* the sensory receptors for hearing. Frequency localization in the cochlea, as well as at all other levels of the auditory pathway, is readily found in laboratory experiments. The *basal turn* of the cochlea, where the sound first enters, is the receptor area for high frequencies. The small canals up in the *apex* of the cochlea receive low frequency stimuli.

Since the hair cell tissue must be removed by dissection and placed under a microscope in order to be seen, no one has ever observed them during the actual hearing process. For this reason the precise behavior of the inner ear must be described hypothetically as "theories of hearing." The earliest of the widely accepted theories of hearing stated that each row of hair cells was tuned to a different frequency, similar to the arrangement of the keys on a piano. For this reason it was called the "piano theory," the "resonance theory," or the "place theory." It was later found that the number of rows of hair cells did not correspond to the number of frequencies heard. Many more hair cells would have been necessary to account for the greater number of frequencies.

Another theory of hearing stated that the sound waves were transmitted through the ear to the cochlea where the sound pattern was simply converted into neural impulses of the same frequencies and sent to the brain. The principle was thought to be similar to that of the telephone, and was therefore termed the "telephone theory," or the "frequency theory." As more neurological information was obtained it was discovered that the auditory nerve would not transmit impulses at a rate greater than 1000 pulses per second. Thus the theory would not account for hearing high pitched sounds.

As a result of the laboratory evidence representing the strength and weaknesses of the two preceding theories, a third theory evolved which combined the best features of the other two. This was called the "volley theory" or sometimes the "combination theory," which was generally accepted through the late 1950's. According to this theory, the frequency principle applied to all sound reception below 1000 Hz., and the place principle applied to sounds above 1000 Hz., thus representing the entire range of human hearing.

The most recent theory as to how frequency distinctions are made is based on the length of the sound wave as it travels through the ear. High frequency waves, being shorter, produce greater excursion of the basilar membrane near the entrance to the cochlea. The longer waves of the low frequencies stimulate the cochlea farther away from the entrance. This has become known as the "traveling wave theory," and because it employs the general principle of frequency location among the rows of hair cells it is also classified as a place theory.

Regardless of the theory involved, it has been established that the sound is introduced into the fluid of the cochlea by means of the piston-like action of the stapes footplate moving against the oval window. The hydraulic waves inside the cochlea cause the tectorial membrane to push against the tiny hairs which protrude above the hair cells. This action causes the hair cells to transmit small neural impulses into the end fibers of the eighth nerve. Careful measurements have found these impulses to be of the order of 80 millivolts (80/1000 volts).

The hair cells are divided into two types—the *internal hair cells* and the *external hair cells*. Most of our hearing appears to take place by means of the external hair cells, since these are the more sensitive. Little is known of the purpose of the internal hair cells, except that they have a higher threshold for sound and are less easily damaged. It is possible that they may somehow account for the recruitment phenomenon in cases of sensori-neural hearing loss.

Immediately after leaving the organ of corti, the neural impulses pass through the *spiral ganglion,* which appears as a turnip-shaped enlargement of the nerve. This bundle apparently acts as a relay station which helps to send the acoustic impulses on up the eighth nerve.

THE AUDITORY PATHWAY

The combined fibers of all the nerves from the organ of corti gather to form the *cochlear branch of the eighth nerve*. Outside the cochlea this branch is joined by the receptor nerves from the semicircular canals and the vestibule, which comprise the *vestibular branch of the eighth nerve*. The two branches of the eighth nerve combine to form one larger trunk at the level of the *internal auditory meatus,* which is a bony tunnel through the skull. The seventh (facial) nerve accompanies the eighth nerve through the same tunnel.

Damage to the eighth nerve is characterized by a hearing loss predominantly in the higher frequencies and an inability to hear pure tones for sustained periods. A frequent cause of damage at this level of the auditory pathway is an acoustic tumor.

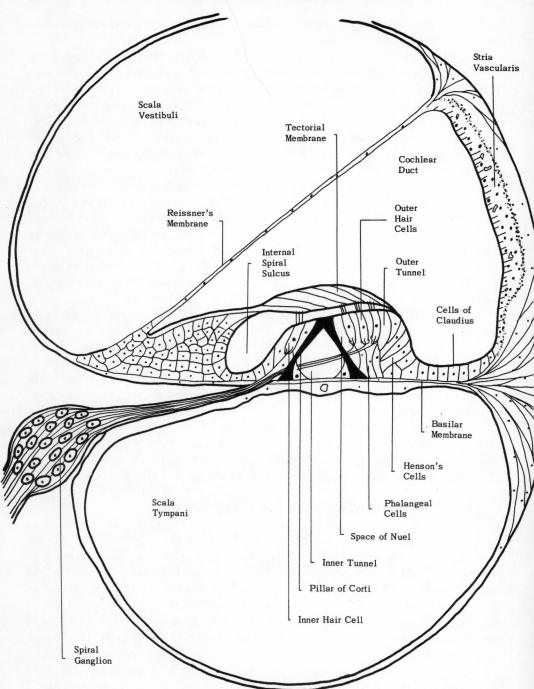

Scala
Vestibuli

Tectorial
Membrane

Stria
Vascularis

Cochlear
Duct

Reissner's
Membrane

Outer
Hair
Cells

Internal
Spiral
Sulcus

Outer
Tunnel

Cells of
Claudius

Basilar
Membrane

Henson's
Cells

Scala
Tympani

Phalangeal
Cells

Space of Nuel

Inner Tunnel

Pillar of Corti

Inner Hair Cell

Spiral
Ganglion

Fig. 51

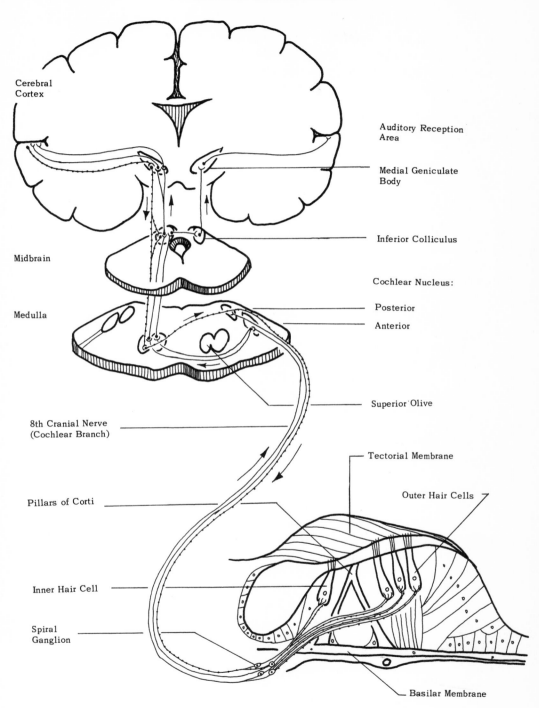

Fig. 52

The *eighth nerve* enters the brain stem at the bottom edge of the *pons*, where it is received by the *cochlear nucleus*. Structurally, the cochlear nucleus is divided into three parts,[1] but most of the incoming signal has been found to pass through the anterior section.

From the cochlear nucleus the stimulus crosses to the opposite side of the nervous system by means of the *trapezoid fibers*, which serve as the connecting links for this part of the auditory pathway. From this point some impulses continue up the brain stem, but many synapse at a nucleus called the *superior olive*. This well-developed nucleus exercises some influence in inhibiting the passage of unwanted incoming sound stimuli.

Above the superior olive the auditory impulse enters the *inferior colliculus*, one of the largest nuclei of the brain stem. Here a good share of the auditory discriminations take place before the cerebral cortex becomes aware of the incoming signal. These discriminations include the turning on or off of sound stimuli, changes in intensity, and changes in frequency. The startle reflex to sudden sound is also mediated in the inferior colliculus.

Slightly higher in the auditory pathway, the impulse enters the *medial geniculate body*, which is a small protrusion at the posterior end of the thalamus. As yet, no specific function can be credited to this nucleus other than that of relay station to the auditory cortex. Between the medial geniculate and the auditory cortex the auditory pathway is not narrowly defined, but rather blends into the general cortical matrix in the form of *auditory radiations*.

The *primary auditory area of the cortex*, located in the temporal lobe of the brain, is important in identifying the direction and location of sounds, and for the discrimination of complex sound patterns, involving differences in timing, pitch, and loudness. It is thus essential for the discrimination of speech symbols.

Information received at the auditory area is relayed to other parts of the cerebral cortex and combined with information from other receptors, providing the individual with a running account of the happenings in his surrounding environment. The mixing of auditory and visual information is particularly evident both in the cortical and subcortical pathways.

An additional aspect of the auditory system which has been discussed very little is the well-defined *descending* or *efferent* tract. This pathway has been traced downward from the auditory cortex all the way to the hair cells, crossing the midline just below the superior olive. Although the precise scope and function of the descending tract is still the subject of investigation, the initial research suggests that it serves as a feedback

---

[1]Rose, J. E.: Organization of frequency sensitive neurons in the cochlear complex of the cat. In *Neural Mechanisms of the Auditory and Vestibular Systems*, Rasmussen, G. L., and W. F. Windle, Eds. Springfield, Thomas, 1960.

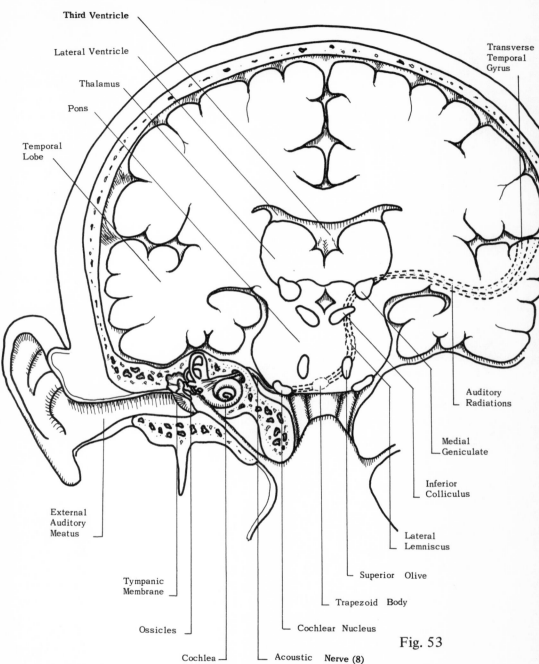

Third Ventricle

Lateral Ventricle

Thalamus

Pons

Temporal
Lobe

Transverse
Temporal
Gyrus

Auditory
Radiations

Medial
Geniculate

Inferior
Colliculus

External
Auditory
Meatus

Lateral
Lemniscus

Superior   Olive

Tympanic
Membrane

Trapezoid   Body

Ossicles

Cochlear   Nucleus

Cochlea

Acoustic   Nerve (8)

Fig. 53

system for the control of incoming stimuli. It appears that efferent impulses from the cortex, mediated through the superior olive, can serve to
reduce incoming sound stimuli at the hair cells. Presumably, the passage
of certain unwanted noise may be inhibited by this arrangement.

APPENDIX 1

In this appendix are presented the Latin derivations of names used in many of the anatomical structures. The student who is familiar with these derivations will find that the names of the muscles are guide posts to their shapes, locations, or functions. For example, the name *serratus posterior superior* means a *saw-toothed* muscle located near the *top* of the *back*, and the *levator palati* refers to a muscle which *raises* the palate. NOTE: The suffix *oid* means form or shape, as in sphen*oid* (wedge-shaped), and cric*oid* (ring-shaped).

ENGLISH WORD	LATIN OR GREEK	ORIGINAL DERIVATION	ORIGINAL MEANING
abdominus	Latin	*abdominus*	abdomen
acoustic	Greek	*akouein*	to hear
acromion	Greek	*akros*	summit
adenoid	Greek	*aden*	gland
alveolar	Latin	*alveolus*	small cavity
anterior	Latin	*anti*	before
arytenoid	Greek	*arytaina*	ladle or pitcher
atlas	Greek	*Atlas*	giant who holds the world
atrium	Latin	*atrium*	a living room
auditory	Latin	*audire*	to hear
axis	Latin	*axis*	axle
carotid	Greek	*karos*	deep sleep
cervical	Latin	*cervix*	neck
chorea	Greek	*choreia*	dance

ENGLISH WORD	LATIN OR GREEK	ORIGINAL DERIVATION	ORIGINAL MEANING
cleido	Greek	*kleis*	key or bar
coccyx	Greek	*kokkyx*	(beak of a) cuckoo
cochlea	Latin	*cochlea*	snail shell
concha	Greek	*kongche*	shell
constrictor	Latin	*constrictus*	squeeze
cornu	Latin	*cornu*	horn
cortex	Latin	*cortex*	bark of a tree
cricoid	Greek	*krikos*	ring
cuneiform	Latin	*cuneus*	wedge (shaped)
di -	Greek	*di*	two
diaphragm	Greek	*diaphragma*	midriff
dorsi	Latin	*dorsum*	back
efferent	Latin	*efferre*	to carry away
epi -	Greek	*epi*	upon
esophagus	Greek	*oisophagus*	gullet
ethmoid	Greek	*ethmoid*	sieve-shaped
external	Latin	*externus*	outside
fascia	Latin	*facies*	face
fascicule	Latin	*fasciculus*	small-bundle
fauces	Latin	*fauces*	jaws or throat
fenestration	Latin	*fenestra*	window
foramen	Latin	*foramin*	hole
fossa	Latin	*fossa*	trench
gastric	Greek	*gaster*	belly
geniculate	Latin	*geniculum*	knee
genio -	Greek	*geneion*	chin

ENGLISH WORD	LATIN OR GREEK	ORIGINAL DERIVATION	ORIGINAL MEANING
gluteus	Latin	*gluteus*	gelatin
helix	Greek	*helix*	coil
humerus	Latin	*humerus*	shoulder
hyoid	Greek	*hyoeides*	Y-shaped
ilium	Latin	*ilium*	flank
incus	Latin	*incusus*	anvil
inferior	Latin	*inferus*	under
inter	Latin	*inter*	between
lamina	Latin	*lamina*	thin plate
lateral	Latin	*latus*	side
latissimus	Latin	*latus*	broad
lemniscus	Greek	*lemniskos*	ribbon
lesion	Latin	*laedere*	injury
levator	Latin	*levare*	to raise
linguae	Latin	*linguae*	tongue
lumbar	Latin	*lumbus*	loin
magnus	Latin	*magnus*	large
malar	Latin	*mala*	cheek
mandible	Latin	*mandibulum*	jaw
masseter	Greek	*masseter*	one that chews
mastoid	Greek	*mastos*	breast
maxilla	Latin	*maxilla*	upper jaw
meatus	Latin	*meatus*	passage
medial	Latin	*medius*	middle
medulla	Latin	*medulla*	narrow
mental	Latin	*mentum*	chin
nucleus	Latin	*nucleous*	nut

ENGLISH WORD	LATIN OR GREEK	ORIGINAL DERIVATION	ORIGINAL MEANING
occipital	Latin	*occiput*	back of the head
omo -	Greek	*omos*	shoulder
oto -	Greek	*otos*	ear
palpebral	Latin	*palpebralis*	eyelid
parietal	Latin	*paries*	side or wall
pectoralis	Latin	*pectus*	breast
pelvis	Latin	*pelvis*	basin
pinna	Latin	*pinna*	feather or fin
pisiform	Latin	*pisum*	pea-shaped
pons	Latin	*pons*	bridge
posterior	Latin	*posterus*	afterward
pterygoid	Greek	*pterygeoides*	winglike
pubes	Latin	*pubes*	maturation
quadratus	Latin	*quadratus*	four-sided
raphe	Greek	*raphe*	seam
rectus	Latin	*rectus*	vertically straight
rhomboid	Greek	*rhomboeides*	rhombohedron
salpingo	Greek	*salpingos*	trumpet
sacrum	Latin	*sacrum*	sacred (bone offered in sacrifices)
scala	Latin	*scala*	staircase
scalene	Greek	*scalenos*	uneven
sclerosis	Greek	*skleros*	hard
septum	Latin	*septum*	a division
serratus	Latin	*serratus*	saw-toothed
sphenoid	Greek	*sphen*	wedge (shaped)
stapes	Latin	*stapes*	stirrup

ENGLISH WORD	LATIN OR GREEK	ORIGINAL DERIVATION	ORIGINAL MEANING
sternum	Latin	*sternum*	chest
styloid	Greek	*stylos*	pillar
sulcus	Latin	*sulcus*	furrow
superior	Latin	*superus*	above
temporal	Latin	*tempora*	temple
tensor	Latin	*tensum*	to stretch
thalamus	Greek	*thalamos*	inner chamber
thyroid	Greek	*thyra*	door
tonsil	Latin	*tonsilla*	little pole
trachea	Greek	*tracheia*	rough
transverse	Latin	*transversus*	directed across
trapezius	Greek	*trapezion*	small table
tympanic	Greek	*tympanon*	drum
uvula	Latin	*uva*	little grape
velum	Latin	*velum*	veil
ventricle	Latin	*ventriculus*	stomach
vomer	Latin	*vomer*	plough share
vertebrae	Latin	*vertebra*	turning point
xiphoid	Greek	*xiphos*	sword-shaped
zygoma	Greek	*zygoma*	yoke

APPENDIX 2

Here the International Phonetic Alphabet is presented in a manner that will enable the beginning student to make the first transition from English to phonetic spelling. For a check on the correct phonetic spelling of most words, the reader is referred to Kenyon and Knott: *A Pronouncing Dictionary of American English*.

SYMBOL		EXAMPLE	
English	Phonetic	English	Phonetic
a	e	age	edʒ
a	ɛ	air	ɛr
a	æ	add	æd
a	ə	account	əkaʊnt
a	a	aunt	ant
a	ɑ	father	faðɚ
b	b	boy	bɔɪ
ch	tʃ	chair	tʃɛr
ch	k	chemist	kɛmɪst
d	d	dog	dɔg
e	i	even	ivən
e	ɪ	edition	ɪdɪʃən
e	ɛ	end	ɛnd
f	f	full	fʊl
g	g	go	go
g	dʒ	gem	dʒɛm

90

SYMBOL		EXAMPLE	
English	Phonetic	English	Phonetic
g	ŋ	ring	rɪŋ
g	ʒ	rouge	ruʒ
h	ɦ	hat	hæt
i	aɪ	ice	aɪs
i	ɪ	it	ɪt
j	dʒ	jam	dʒæm
k	k	key	ki
l	l	lamp	læmp
l	l̩	turtle	tɝtl̩
m	m	man	mæn
m	m̩	atom	ætm̩
n	n	name	nem
n	n̩	written	rɪtn̩
n	ŋ	bank	bæŋk
o	o	old	old
o	ɔ	offer	ɔfɚ
o	ɑ	odd	ɑd
o	ə	occur	əkɝ
oi	ɔɪ	oil	ɔɪl
oo	u	ooze	uz
oo	ʊ	look	lʊk
ou	aʊ	out	aʊt
p	p	pig	pɪg
qu	kw	quick	kwɪk
r	r	rope	rop
r	ɝ	earth	ɝθ

## SYMBOL	EXAMPLE

English	Phonetic	English	Phonetic
r	ɚ	over	ovɚ
s	s	so	so
s	ʃ	sugar	ʃʊgɚ
s	ʒ	measure	mɛʒɚ
s	z	chairs	tʃɛrz
sh	ʃ	shoe	ʃu
t	t	time	taɪm
th	θ	three	θri
th	ð	these	ðiz
u	u	rude	rud
u	ʊ	put	pʊt
u	ju	use	juz
u	ʌ	under	ʌndɚ
v	v	voice	vɔɪs
w	w	win	wɪn
w	hw	why	hwaɪ
x	ks	six	sɪks
y	j	yes	jɛs
z	z	zoo	zu

INDEX

A

Abdominal cavity, 4
Acoustic nerve, 83
Acromion process, 61
Adam's apple, 45
Alveolar process, 11
Anderson, V. A., 47
Anterior palatine fossa, 13
Aorta, 22
Apex, 78
Articulation, 55
Arytenoid cartilage, 41, 42, 43, 44
Atlas, 10, 24, 31
Atresia, 74
Auditory radiations, 82, 83
Auditory reception area, 81
Axis, 10, 24
Auditory meatus, 12

B

Basal turn, 78
Basilar membrane, 80, 81
Breathing, 3

C

Cancer of the larynx, 51
Carrell, J., 57
Cells of Claudius, 80
Cerebral cortex, 81
Cerebral palsy, 3
Ceruman, 74
Cervical vertebrae, 6, 10
Chorda tympani, 75
Clavical, 9, 27
Clavicular breathing, 3
Coccyx, 9, 10
Cochlea, 78
Cochlear duct, 77, 80
Cochlear nerve, 76, 77
Cochlear nucleus, 81, 82, 83
Condyle of the mandible, 12
Consonants, 56
Constrictor muscles, 60, 67
Coracoid process, 61
Coranoid process, 12
Corniculate cartilage, 42
Cornu, 6

Coronal suture, 11
Cricoid cartilage, 40, 41, 42, 43, 46, 62
Cricothyroid, 47, 48, 49

D

Descending auditory tract, 82
Diaphragm, 3, 4, 21, 22, 27
Diagastric, 58, 62
Dorsal vertebrae, 10

E

Ear canal, 74
Ear drum, 38, 39, 74
Efferent auditory tract, 82
Eighth nerve, 77, 79, 81
Epiglottis, 40, 41, 50
Esophageal speech, 51, 52
Esophagus, 22, 27, 52, 60
Eustachian tube, 16, 76, 78
Exhalation, 4, 5, 28
External auditory meatus, 12, 15, 16, 62,
      76, 83
External hair cells, 79
External oblique, 28, 29, 30

F

Facial nerve, 76
Fairbanks, G., 45
Fifth cranial nerve, 12
Floating ribs, 9
Fluctuations in speech, 45
Foramen magnum, 13, 16
Forced exhalation, 5, 6
Froeschels, E., 49
Frontal bone, 12, 62
Frontal sinus, 14

G

Genioglossus, 58, 59, 68
Geniohyoid, 58, 68
Greater palatine foramen, 13

H

Hair Cells, 78
Hard palate, 13, 14, 16

93

Vestibular nerve, 76, 77
Vocal cords, 44
Vocal intensity, 3
Vocalis, 44, 47
Volley theory, 78
Vowels, 55

W

Westlake, H., 3
Wynder, D. L., 51

X, Y, Z

Zygomatic arch, 9, 11